The Wisdom of Canute

Published in 2016 by Canterbury Christ Church University
North Holmes Road, Canterbury, Kent CT1 1QU

ISBN 978-1-909067-58-5

Creative Writing Workshops are part of the Community Arts and Education programme offered by the Faculty of Education at Canterbury Christ Church University (CCCU). These diverse groups are made up of students with varying degrees of writing experience.

For the summer 2016 anthology, we are pleased to offer you a collection of short stories, flash fiction and poetry.

April Doyle
Tutor and Editor

Contents

The Wisdom of Canute

Caroline Cannons

As you can see, I am attached to this bench. It is the custodian of a thousand happy memories. Every knot, every shake, every check in the wood enhances its value. Brush your hand along its ageing body, washed clean by each high tide. Does it speak to you? I sense that you do not appreciate it as I do. Please, sit with me. Grant me a few moments longer of your time. Let me convince you of its worth.

Close your eyes and listen to the roar of the advancing waves. The growls and rumbles grow louder as the sea rushes to greet us. We eagerly await the moment when its waves crash below our feet. There. Taste the salt of the spray and feel the warmth of the sun's rays as they dry your face. You must agree, it is wonderful.

And much like her, it is untameable.

Six years ago my wife Angela, and I took an uncharacteristic leap of faith – we left behind our rather grand family home in suburban London, and relocated to the cosy chalet bungalow you see behind us. We down-sized, I think the younger generation says.

Our children had long since moved out, and set up home with their own friends or partners, but they remained nostalgic for the family home. Friends ridiculed our decision to move, bleating on and on that we would miss the razzmatazz of our social network. They were convinced we would return as soon as the monotony of provincial life here on the south east coast became our reality. 'Sleepyville will not suit you,' they'd said. 'We'll give you a six months. A year, tops,' they'd said.

Bets were made as to how long we would survive the 'sluggish pace of life' before lethargy took hold and we scurried back to the high-octane life of West London.

If only I had captured on canvas our children's expressions as they reacted to our news - I could have set up my own portrait gallery and charged a small fortune for admission! George, our eldest, would be the boldest picture, painted in the bright hue of squashed raspberries, clashing violently with his auburn hair; such an ugly portrait. He challenged us at each stage of the move, and his sneers wounded. I could have tolerated his infernal guffaws when he first saw what we had bought, but then he proceeded to lecture us about our dereliction of duty as grandparents and the dissipation of family wealth. Well, it was really all about *his* inheritance in the end. Angela was shocked. It upset her more than she was prepared to admit. You see, George is the first born of our four children, and the father of our granddaughter. I also suspect that he was Angela's favourite. Until then.

Our twins, Martha and Ruth, were abroad, on a gap year after completing their respective degrees in art and drama. As we were happy to continue bank-rolling their travels, our move did not affect them much. Their portraits would be abstract creations - fluffy cloud formations, randomly placed on a purple canvas. The word *inheritance* could never be a part of their shared vocabulary. They are thrill-seekers, and have always been so, since we first took them to Disneyland at the age of four; our whitecap surfers of life. So much like their mother.

Our younger son, David, is a physician. He would be drawn in the muted shades of an impressionist painter, reflecting a more caring, sensitive man. Although he too joined in with the banter, I believe that he understood why we sought a less frenetic pace of life - so he quietly helped us with the practicalities of the move and continues to visit, when he can.

Initially, Angela and I commuted to work. Granted, it was a much longer journey than before, but it was fun travelling in by train together. During the outward journey we worked in companionable silence, preparing notes for our day ahead. The return journey was more fun. We would compete to be the first to finish a crossword or mathematical puzzle. Angela always won the word challenges - only to be expected I suppose, with her first in English. I am sharper, more logical with the maths puzzles, although she did beat me once, completing a number challenge by the time we had pulled out of the station! Then, we would think about what we would like to do later that evening, stopping off at the local supermarket to pick up some provisions as we left the station.

Inevitably, I cooked whilst Angela luxuriated in the bath, sipping a glass or two of chilled wine. We usually dined around eight o'clock, then lounged in front of a log fire in the winter, or sat out on the balcony in warmer weather, looking onto the refreshing waters of the English Channel. By ten o'clock we would be entwined in each other's arms, our love-making taking us through to the early hours of the morning.

She was insatiable…

I notice that I have caused you some embarrassment, but I make no excuses. You see, affection must be expressed. Angela showed me that, in the first few months of our relationship. We may have been married for over forty years, but passion is not solely for youth, you know.

From the outset, I knew that she would be the girl I would marry. It was an unusually sunny Monday afternoon, during my first term at Cambridge...

I watch as a slender goddess glides towards me, dressed in a full-length cheesecloth skirt and long-sleeved tee-shirt. Her long hair absorbs the late autumn sun, and radiates a light that frames her English rose complexion. She is reading from a book that is precariously balanced on a stack in her arms. As she passes me, she falters and drops the pile. 'Let me help you,' I say. And as I bend down, our fingers brush and we catch our breath, awakening a desire that has never diminished.

Angela introduced me to a brighter world; one that was so different to my austere beginnings. She was so much more adventurous. Do you know, her exuberant nature almost got her sent down? She appeared before the Dean on more than one occasion, I can tell you! Yes, my Angela lived life to the edge and I was a moth to her flame...

Eventually, the commute became wearisome and so we started to seek employment nearer home. It did not take long for either of us to find work with local companies. We no longer wished to chase obscene salaries. We had all that we needed.

Our family came to visit; sometimes for a day or two, sometimes longer. Even George began to appreciate the inner peace this home offers. But, despite our much healthier lifestyle - leisurely walks in the summer, brisker ones in the bracing winter months - Angela's health began to wane.

Her flawless skin lost its youthful shine. Her eyes lost their sparkle...

Here's a photograph of Angela on her sixtieth birthday. Beautiful, isn't she? It is one of my favourites, taken the last time the family was all together. When everything was how it should be. You must agree – we resemble an odd jigsaw; each piece is unique but plays a vital part to the whole. The ruddy-faced one is George, of course.

We established a comfortable routine. Once a week, usually on a Saturday, Angela prepared a meal for the two of us. She used every saucepan, piece of crockery and cooking utensil we possess to create her masterpieces, but they tasted truly divine. Italian food was her speciality, and she would have a glass of red wine at her elbow as she cooked, singing arias from her favourite opera, Puccini's Madame Butterfly, filling every corner of the house with her rich mezzo-soprano voice. We have a small dining table that nestles in the upper bay window, the one that overlooks the beach, and we'd often listen to a Bach prelude or Mozart symphony. We talked, as if we have not seen each other for months, unaware that the shadows cast by the flickering candle were also a portent.

Unlike Canute, Angela could sometimes stem the tide of conversation, but silence was never uncomfortable. We'd listen to the waves as they rolled in to reclaim stones from the beach. In the summer months, we'd retire to bed at dusk, allowing the sea's lullaby to pull us into its embrace…

When Angela's illness was finally diagnosed we had already been here five years. Neither of us wanted to move back to London, nor did we want to share the news. We were afraid it would make it too real.

That first Easter we booked a cottage retreat in Cornwall. We wanted to hide away from the rest of the world. Ironically, it was fun

11

deciding what to do with the time we have left together. She made it so. We became adventurers preparing for the most important expedition of our lives. Our priority was each other. So, on our return, we took early retirement.

Angela adapted more quickly than I to this leisurely pace of life, but she coaxed and cajoled. We strolled around the gardens at Walmer Castle at least once a week and occasionally indulged in an afternoon cream tea. Here she is straddling one of the cannons. She fell off immediately after I took that photograph. We were later told that her laughter could be heard in the keep!

Angela's russet hair lost its lustre. Each morning we would wake up to yet another handful of her greying locks on the pillow. We called them pixie parcels and laughed about it. What else could we do?

When our walks became too challenging, our home help brought her spaniel to visit. Henry has been a welcome distraction. He loves Angela, almost as much as I do.

Please!

I am aware that you are restless to get on with your work, but give me a few more moments. I'm almost finished.

This past month Angela's world has shrivelled to the confines of our home. The distance to this bench is the farthest she will shuffle from the garden. Each day, we come here to welcome the tides. We sit and reminisce. Sometimes we sit in peaceful harmony, trying to catch sight of what lies beyond the horizon.

But always on this bench.

No other seat will do.

Every knot, every shake, every check in the wood comforts her. The sea comes to release her, and with each crashing wave her pain is eased. Do you hear the gulls? They are announcing her arrival.

Here she is. My beautiful, brave wife.

Now, if you would be so kind as to pass me my blanket, I will consent to your request and unshackle my wrist from the frame of this bench. After all, I do not wish to alarm Angela. All I ask of you and your colleagues is that you return to the planning department and request delaying the reconstruction of this section of the beach. Allow me to sit with my wife, until God decides it is time.

For, as you can see, it will be soon.

Walking for Charity
Valerie Moffit

The straps of the rucksack are cutting into her shoulders and her feet are throbbing. What's worse, she can feel an ominous but familiar ache in her lower stomach. 'Shall we have a rest here?'

Sandra nods eagerly and they both flop down onto the roadside verge. Although the sun is warmer now, the grass still feels damp and so they spread out their jackets to sit on. Penny unfastens the buckles on her rucksack and produces a greaseproof parcel, unwrapping it to reveal egg and tomato sandwiches, prepared by her mother at six o'clock this morning. There's also a small bottle of orange squash, and two custard creams.

'Oh yum,' says Sandra through a mouthful of sandwich.

'I don't think I've ever been so hungry,' says Penny.

They sit under the hawthorn hedge for a while. All is silent except for a blackbird singing, and Penny thinks how lovely it would be just to spend the rest of the day here.

'How far do you think we've come?' wonders Sandra.

'We've been walking for two hours,' Penny says. 'Maybe about ten miles?'

'Hmm.' Sandra is doubtful. 'More likely six or seven, I'd say.' She wrinkles her nose. 'Eugh, what's that smell?'

They get reluctantly to their feet and Penny investigates along the hedge bottom. 'It's a dead rabbit,' she says, stepping back. 'Looks like it had myxomatosis.'

'Poor thing!'

'It's a horrible disease.' Penny's ambition is to be a vet. 'They get tumours on their eyes and go blind before they die.'

'God, that's awful,' shudders Sandra. 'Let's get away from here.'

Nearly forty girls from Penny and Sandra's school are taking part in a fund-raising walk for Oxfam. They started at eight this morning, from a village somewhere north of Rothbury, where Tait's bus dropped them. They've been given a sketch map with directions marked on it, showing the route to Morpeth.

'The others have left us behind. Rotten lot.'

'Alison and Hilary started off much too fast,' says Penny. 'Showing off. They'll soon get tired, and then we'll catch them up.' She's not sure she believes this.

The sixth-formers nominated to lead the walk are Alison Kent, Head Girl and hockey captain, and Hilary Bentall, who always wins the 100 metres hurdles at Sports Day. It's clear that they're determined to beat everyone else. Penny and Sandra hate athletics and loathe hockey.

'Who cares if we come last?' says Sandra. 'It's not a competition.'

Penny says grimly, 'And, guess what? I've got my period.'

Sandra sympathises. 'There's fish paste sandwiches in my bag, but maybe we should save them for later.'

The mention of fish paste sandwiches reminds Penny to ask after Sandra's mother, as her own mother has told her to.

'How's your Mam?' she enquires.

'She's in hospital,' Sandra says quietly, her face clouding. Penny can tell she doesn't want to talk about it.

Sandra's mother Doreen had been a dancer before she met and married Phil Roberts. Now, she is sometimes to be seen in the tiny back office at Roberts' Garage, working out the men's wages and bringing the accounts up to date. On other days she stays in bed. Recently, when Penny called at the house for Sandra, she found Mrs Roberts sitting at the kitchen table with a glass of whisky in front of her. She didn't respond to Penny's greeting. She's unreachable, thought Penny – immersed in her own private darkness.

Now Penny says to Sandra, 'Those fish paste sandwiches sound like a good idea.' They share one companionably as they stroll along in the sunshine.

Minutes later, a car approaches.

'Oh hell, it's Gammy!'

It is indeed Miss Grenville, the Headmistress, in her green Hillman Minx. She glides to a halt by Sandra and Penny and, winding down her window, beams beneficently at them.

'You're rather a long way behind the others,' she remarks in a jovial manner. 'Have some chocolate!' She offers each of them a small bar of Dairy Milk.

'Thank you, Miss Grenville,' they mumble, amazed to see the Head in such good humour. At school, she is usually simmering with disapproval as she hands out reprimands for minor misdeeds. Handing out chocolate bars is not part of Gammy's usual routine.

Still, thinks Penny, it's Saturday, so Miss Grenville's off duty. And so are they, for that matter; but they've volunteered, along with most of their classmates in 3W, to do the twenty-five-mile charity walk.

They've each persuaded aunts and grandparents to sponsor them at a penny or tuppence a mile.

'You're doing splendidly, girls! Keep up your pace and I'll see you at the Town Hall.' Miss Grenville executes a rapid three-point turn and, waving gaily, drives off in a cloud of exhaust.

'Blimey,' says Sandra. They trudge on, savouring the chocolate as it melts slowly, deliciously, on their tongues. 'She won't be so friendly when we mess up the handshakes next week.'

Penny laughs, remembering that a ritual ordeal is planned for them on Tuesday.

Miss Grenville sets great store by good manners and a smart appearance, and every girl in the school is required to endure a regular Deportment Test. There is a long-established route - beginning in the assembly hall, going up the north stairs, following the top corridor past the geography room, and finally descending the south stairs. At each crucial point along the way a teacher sits with a notebook, jotting down marks for how well each girl holds her head up, keeps a straight back climbing and descending the stairs, and whether she says 'Good morning' with a polite smile. The Deportment Test culminates, naturally, with Miss Grenville. Outside the Head's study two chairs are placed, and there the candidates wait, in pairs, sick with trepidation. When called, each pair enters the inner sanctum, closing the door quietly behind them. Girl A first introduces her partner, girl B, to the Headmistress; and then she introduces Miss G to her partner. A firm handshake is required. Next it is girl B's turn to repeat the performance. The whole process is fraught with pitfalls, and woe betide she who gets her introductions tangled.

'What about Maggie, last year?' chuckles Sandra. Maggie Hayle – a fifth former who by common consent is the sexiest girl in the school – had made a complete hash of the Deportment Test's climax. In sheer frustration she'd yelled 'Fuck this!', burst into uproarious laughter, and slammed out of Gammy's study.

'What's it all for?' wonders Sandra now. 'Does Gammy think we're all going to marry dukes and get presented to the Queen?'

'Yeah, I'll call my memoir *From pit village to palace*. It'll be a best-seller!'

'But everyone knows I'm going to marry John Lennon,' says Sandra. 'You can have George,' she tells Penny magnanimously.

It is more than an hour since the chocolate encounter, and Penny and Sandra still haven't caught up with the rest of the walkers. Every time they crest a hill or round a bend, Penny expects to see some other stragglers up ahead, but is disappointed. She realises Sandra is beginning to lose heart – she keeps swearing under her breath – and to be honest Penny feels desperate too. Her blisters are agony and the dragging pain in her belly is worse. She can feel blood oozing through the makeshift pad of toilet paper that she's stuffed into her pants. They have also finished the fish paste sandwiches and custard creams.

'Let's have another look at the map,' says Sandra. She studies it; turns it upside down; looks worried. 'Do you remember that fork in the road, a while back? I think maybe we should have gone right instead of left.'

'Oh shit,' groans Penny and collapses slowly onto the long grass by the roadside. 'Just let me die now.'

'Hang on - I can hear a car,' says Sandra suddenly, and they both hold their breath. The noise of the engine grows louder, and around the bend just ahead cruises a large black Ford. 'It's Dad!'

As the car pulls up, Penny sees that it is not Mr Roberts at the wheel but his apprentice mechanic, Jimmy Slater.

'Your Dad sent me out to look for you,' he tells Sandra with a smirk, leaning out of the driver's window. 'Good job, cos you're miles behind the others. Hop in and I'll take you the rest of the way.'

Jimmy is Penny's least favourite person. Last week, when she called at Roberts' Garage for Sandra, he'd pushed against her in a doorway and grabbed her left breast. It was over so quickly that she almost disbelieved it had happened. She was left confused and furious but also, unaccountably, ashamed. Now he grins in her direction and says, 'Alright, Penny?' She flushes and looks away, disgusted by his black fingernails and greasy Elvis hairdo.

Sandra says to Jimmy, 'You can't take us all the way to the Town Hall, because Hilary and Alison will disqualify us for cheating. Then all this hell we've been through will be wasted.'

Jimmy shrugs. 'Suit yourself. What's the plan, then?'

He and Sandra confer while Penny closes her eyes and imagines herself at home in a hot bath. She realises that she couldn't care less whether they cheat or not.

'Here's what we'll do,' she interrupts. 'We'll lie flat on the back seat of the car so no-one sees us. And when Jimmy gets to a gap between two groups of walkers, he can stop and let us out.'

Sandra looks uncertain.

'It'll be fine,' Penny reassures her, 'as long as Jimmy drops us well up the line, not too far from the finish. You can keep a secret, can't you, Jimmy?' she says, holding his gaze.

He hesitates for a moment, disconcerted. Then, 'Yeah. Okay,' he says.

'Good. And all we have to do is brazen it out,' she tells Sandra. 'No-one need ever know.'

'Right,' says Sandra, suddenly resolute. 'Let's do it.'

Penny and Sandra finally hobble into the Town Hall, not far behind the leaders. They collect their certificates from Miss Grenville, who gives them each a firm handshake and says, 'Well done, girls! Slow and steady does it, like Aesop's tortoise.' They have no clue what she's on about.

Alison Kent and Hilary Bentall do a double take. 'Where did you two spring from?' asks Alison suspiciously.

Penny looks her in the eye. 'Oh we were saving ourselves, and then we put on a bit of a spurt at the end. Didn't we, Sand?'

Sandra raises her chin and says, 'Yes we did, Pen.'

Indifference

Carol Hyde

From the French doors, I can see the small family picnicking in Dane John Gardens. Mum, Dad, a little boy who looks to be about two years old, and Grandma. I'm not sure which side of the family she belongs, no one is paying her much attention, as it's all on the little boy. I think they're Japanese.

As I turn back to what I'm doing, I notice Grandma rolling a ball along the ground to the child, who toddles over, and picks it up delightedly.

'Bring it to Grandma', she calls, or at least that's what I imagine she says, because she isn't speaking English. The parents, sitting on a rug close by, call to their son and point to Grandma. The little one has a wicked grin and starts running away with the ball. Grandma pretends to run after him, stomping her feet.

'I'm going to catch you,' I guess she's saying, because he squeals with delight and runs away, almost faster than his little legs can carry him.

Enough gazing out the window, I've got so much packing to do. I'm moving into a retirement home at the end of the week and I have to work through thirty-seven years of accumulation to decide what is going with me, and what to give away. Thirty-seven years of marriage, two sons, two trial separations and re-unions, and a final divorce.

David said he wanted to do more with his life – travel, take up dancing, find a hobby. But I was never really interested in all that. All I wanted, once the boys had left home, was to stop mothering him – picking up after him, cooking and cleaning for him, with never a thank you or an offer to help. Women's work, he called it. Thank goodness those days are gone.

The funny thing is, he never did do any travel or dancing once we were divorced. But he did take up fishing, which makes me laugh. People always say it's cheaper to buy the fish than pay for the rod, reel and bait. But David gave up his house and paid divorce lawyers just to go fishing. I don't think he ever really knew what he wanted.

He found himself a girlfriend after leaving me. She moved in with him, and eventually – or should I say, inevitably – she moved out again. She told him she hadn't moved in just to be his housekeeper.

He was diagnosed with pancreatic cancer a few months later and spent his remaining time in and out of hospital – more in than out, really. He wasn't such a bad person. Just a bit lost really.

I still have a framed photo of him on my sideboard. I refused to put it away when he first moved out, because I was done with cleaning up after him. I must have thought he'd take it with him on one of his several trips back to the house to collect his things. Then, when he was dying, I thought if I put it away, it would look like I was trying to hasten his death. So in the end it just stayed there. My only concession is that when I do the cleaning, I dust everything on the sideboard except that photo. Oh well, hopefully one of my sons, Robert or Leslie, it doesn't matter which, will take it with them when I leave here.

The problem with this packing business is that every time I empty out a cupboard, I find something that distracts me from what I'm supposed to be doing. I get lost in photos for hours. Wedding photos, mine and my sons', baby photos and photos of grandchildren, holiday snaps, black and white polaroids, pictures of my parents and sisters, and even photos of my in-laws. David couldn't be bothered to take those.

Now another hour has gone by while I've flicked through yet more albums. I have to take them with me, no-one one else will want them, and I can't throw them out. I don't know how long I've been staring out of the window, lost in reveries, before I become aware of the little Japanese boy and his grandmother again. She is trying to get him to settle down on the rug for a nap.

The parents are nowhere in sight. Grandma's been abandoned, and she looks so tired and lonely. I think she could do with a good cup of tea. I wonder how long the parents have been gone. Where did they go? Shopping? The pub? To visit friends? I feel for Grandma, a woman on her own, taken on a family outing. She thinks it's because they enjoy her company, but the truth is, she is just a convenient babysitter.

The longer I stand here watching her, the more distressed she seems to be. Maybe I should go out and ask if she's OK. Or maybe I could just stroll past and take a closer look. Sitting by her grandson, she seems to half bend and half fall forward, as if she's nodding off to sleep. Then she jerks her head up again and looks around frantically. I guess she's hoping to see her family returning.

She'll be all right. They can't be too far away; it will be getting dark soon. No, I have to get some more packing done before Robert comes over, to stack the boxes for me. He promised to ring me this morning to let me know when he is coming. It's now four in the afternoon and he still hasn't called. Typical. No doubt he'll turn up when it suits him – if he remembers.

I draw the curtains with one last look at Grandma. She's lying down on her side now. I think she's fallen asleep, poor dear.

Right, I'll put the kettle on for a cuppa, while I pack a few more boxes. Then I'll think about dinner. I wonder if I can talk Robert into staying for a bite to eat. Probably not. He's always in a hurry to be somewhere else.

So the albums go on the 'keep' pile. No more time wasting. What's next? I know, glasses. How many should I take with me? I have so many I never use, even some that were wedding presents, and a boxed up set of cocktail glasses I bought for a special occasion, used once, and pushed to the back of the cupboard. There's my nice silver cutlery service too. Only used for special occasions, which are few and far between. I don't think I'll have room for it in the new flat. The problem is I'll feel guilty if I give it to one son and not the other. Then again, the truth is, neither one of them will want it anyway.

Finally, I hear a car pull up outside. Robert at last. Good, I've just about run out of bench and floor space with all the packing boxes, so it will be good to have him pack some of them up high for me, ready for the moving van on Friday. He can take the rest away to the charity shops. As he comes down the hall I call out, 'Robert, would you like this silver cutlery service?'

Before entering the room he replies, 'No thanks Mum, we don't need it'. No surprise there then.

'I can't stay long. Just have time to load up the car and go'. I can't remember the last time he visited me without saying those words the first minute he walked in the door. I show him which boxes are for the charity shops and he immediately starts carrying them out to the car.

After his third trip out and back again, I ask him if he would like a cup of tea.

'Mum, I really don't have time.'

'You are going to stack the rest of the boxes, aren't you?'

'I didn't realise there was so much stuff. Once I've finished loading the car, I have to leave. We're going out tonight.'

'But I can hardly get around the room anymore. I need help to make some space.'

'Can't do it Mum, it'll have to be another day. How about I come around after work tomorrow? I could spend another hour then, if you like.' With that he picks up a box and heads down the hall again.

When he comes back in, he goes straight to the French doors and opens the curtains. Only then do I notice the flashing lights. 'What's going on Rob?'

'Looks like some old bird is sick. Oh no, look, they've drawn a sheet up over her face. Well, you don't see that every day do you? Someone dying outside your door.'

I stand beside him and watch. I can see the Japanese couple and their little boy, but not Grandma. The husband is holding his crying son and trying to comfort his wife.

Oh dear, I didn't really think she looked that bad, just tired and anxious, that's all. Maybe I should have gone out and checked on her. Still what could I have done? She probably couldn't speak English anyway. It's their fault, they shouldn't have gone off and left her. It's got nothing to do with me.

Robert shrugs dismissively and pulls the curtains closed again and lifts another box. 'This is the last one I can fit in the car, Mum.' Grandma is forgotten.

'OK love, thanks for helping. I'll see you tomorrow then.' He pecks me on the cheek and leaves carrying the box.

I return to the window to see what's happening. The ambulance is driving away, and a policeman is talking to the couple. You just never know when your time's up, do you? And when your time's up there's nothing you can do about it.

I wonder what they'll do for a babysitter now.

A Private Life
Carole Lynch

A shaft of sunlight penetrates the grey clouds overhead. The glare blinds him to its warmth, so Darren pulls the net curtain across the window. He looks out from his sparsely furnished front room at the narrow cul-de-sac that is Hillcrest Road. His view to the left only extends as far as the student house halfway down, and to the right ends with the boarded-up flats. Darren stares across at the curtains of number 12. Was that a twitch? Mrs Patel is rarely seen outside her home. And he sits here often enough to know. Reg said something about her husband only allowing her to go to the market once a week. Does she sit hour after hour, hoping to see someone go by, a friendly neighbour who might wave to her? He wants to shout 'Why do you stay in there? Just WALK out.'

The noise of revving shifts his focus onto the helmeted figure from number 18, who is trying to manoeuvre his red Yamaha onto the road between two parked cars. The bike is clearly too heavy for him. Darren feels as though he's been punched, quickly looks away; since the accident he just can't go there. He swings his chair round abruptly so he faces inwards.

He is on the football field dribbling up the left wing, hips swerving like Giggsie. Body turned, he strokes the ball into the back of the net. It's a goal! The crowd goes mad, standing as one, the cheer roaring upwards. Other players are running towards him, patting him on the back, hugging like girls, piling in, and for the moment, he's at the centre of it all.

The cat jumps onto his bony lap and begins to knead his thighs with open claws, snagging the denim of his jeans. Darren shoves her off, wants to kick her. But no movement follows the thought. He grips the wheels of his chair and, white knuckled, swings himself round and round and round until his head is full only of dizziness.

Darren scrolls through the messages on his iPhone. He notices that the interval between texts from his old friends is getting longer. The last one, from best mate Gareth, was two weeks ago. They'd all been off to play five-a-side footie, asked him to come along to referee. Seriously? Darren re-reads his reply. 'Don't need your pity lads, thanks'. Oh, stupid, stupid thing to say. The sound of the opening front door distracts him.

'It's only me, Darren,' calls Reg from the hall.

'Good to see you. I need to go to HMV, if you're up to it, old man?'

'Less of your cheek boy, or we may not get that far.'

They both laugh, at ease with each other as the banter goes back and forth, while they busy themselves with the getting ready to go out routine.

The High Street is bustling and Reg has to negotiate buggies and kids on scooters as he pushes the wheelchair up the hill. He leads with his chin, has a wiry strength that's unexpected given that he's in his seventies. Darren refers to him as 'my volunteer silver fox'. Reg rather enjoys that. Occasionally they stop as he has a quick word with people he knows. Most of them ignore Darren and talk over his head. Reg waves to a young woman holding the hand of a four year-old who has the words 'I'm Cute' on her pink top. They come over.

'Darren, meet Briony. She's my son's partner.'

She says a cursory hello, then she and Reg begin to discuss a forthcoming family wedding. The child stands close to Darren and looks up at him.

'And what's your name?' he says, and smiles.

'Grace,' she says, and smiles back. She comes closer, rests her elbows on the arm of the chair and regards him. Darren is touched and, without thought pushes a lock of hair out of the girl's eyes. He looks at the scruffy teddy she's holding. 'Does your bear have a name, Grace?'

Briony swoops down like a hawk and grabs her daughter, giving Darren a warning glare.

'We'll be off then, Reg.' High heels make a sharp commentary as she clicks-clacks to the shops, perfect ponytail swinging, mobile in one hand and child in the other.

Grace looks back as she's dragged away.

Darren sighs. 'But I was only…'

Reg puts a hand down onto his shoulder. 'I know, lad. It's the times we live in. Nothing at all to do with you.'

The barista in the coffee shop takes a sharp intake of breath as Darren comes in and is settled at a nearby table. As she always does, has been doing for months, she steals frequent glances at him as she prepares the order. Her hands move automatically at the machine, tamping down the granules, switching on the water. All she's conscious of is Darren's broad shoulders and the way his biceps and chest sculpt his tee-shirt. She longs to feel his arms around her, see his eyes admiring her not caring that she is much too fond of cake. She raises her eyes again. Darren has, at last, noticed her and is returning her gaze. The pulse in her neck jumps. But no! He's seeing only the uniform, not the hunger. His look is defiant, shuttered. The girl, red faced, turns quickly away as if scalded and fumbles with the cup in her hand. It crashes to the floor. She tries to gather up the fragments, hardly knowing what she's doing; tries not to cry.

Darren says nothing as he and Reg drink their coffees. The silence lengthens.

'What's up?' says the older man.

'Why do people have to bloody stare – haven't they seen a cripple before?'

'Darren, come on! I think she actually fancies you.'

Darren snorts. 'Yeah, course she does. All anyone sees is the chair.'

Reg leans forward. 'Not everyone. Not my Grace.'

Darren's coffee tastes bitter and he pushes it away. 'She is only four.'

A box on the laptop screen asks whether he wants to play. Darren hesitates. He's bored, with everything, even with himself. Life is crap. The virtual world of Second Life has been mentioned in chatrooms. It won't cost him anything to join. Maybe he'll make new friends, get a girlfriend even. He's heard that sometimes the people behind avatars fall in love in virtual reality, meet up in real life and actually get married. And, most important, he can be whoever he wants to be. He clicks. The avatar he chooses is male, a good physical match to himself, more handsome perhaps. But this version has a job as a personal trainer so works out at the gym, plays football with his mates every week and goes to nightclubs to meet women. He's also the proud owner of a Harley-Davidson. More clicks and the screen changes as Darren joins the virtual community.

A few days later, Reg comes round as usual. He notices the dark circles under Darren's eyes, the coffee stains on his jumper.

'You look wrecked, lad. Aren't you sleeping well?'

Darren takes the laptop off his knees and puts it on the table. 'Too busy meeting people to sleep, mate.'

Reg frowns. 'How do you mean?'

'There's this place just like a real town, only it's online. I can go anywhere I want, any time I want. It's pure bloody magic.'

Reg sits down, leans forward. 'Where do you go then?'

'Well last night, I was at a nightclub chatting up a girl called Rosie. We danced 'til the early hours. She's really nice.' Darren grins, yawns and rubs his eyes.

'It's not real though, is it?' says Reg, struggling to understand.

'The avatars aren't of course, but the people behind them are, like me.'

Reg rubs his chin. 'So who are you then, when you're there?'

'I'm Jake. How cool is that?'

Reg stands up. 'Better get going then, before it rains, eh?'

The sky is deep grey and Reg pushes the chair faster in the diminishing light. They are nearly at the coffee shop. Darren tells Reg to go on to the next one.

Just as they hurry past, the girl looks up and sees him, watches them out of sight. She feels sick. Wants to run after him, to say sorry, that it's all her fault. It's the first time he hasn't come in. She doesn't know what to do. Hoping to see him has become her reason for getting up in the morning. She promises God that if they come in again, she will never eat another piece of cake – or chocolate even. Why, oh, why hasn't she found the courage to say something to him? The air is thick with the weight of disappointment. Down comes the rain.

During the next couple of weeks, Darren hardly bothers to check his phone, calls no one, not even his mum. She leaves him a voicemail message. Reg comes round, as usual, and they go into town. Darren talks incessantly of the people he's meeting. He has a girlfriend. He says her name is Tanya.

'We meet in this pub, it's a themed one, a bit artificial like they all are. It's the Wild West with sawdust on the floor and those swing doors. S'another world in there.'

'You need to switch off that damn machine, lad. Who else have you seen this week apart from me?'

'I've just told you Matt.'

'It's Reg and I rest my case.'

Darren turns his head. 'Sorry. I'm tired. It's all this clubbing.'

Reg pushes the chair in silence. His thumb worries at the rubber on the handle. The hill seems much steeper today.

Darren dials the landline number and taps the table repeatedly with his index finger as he waits. The call is answered.

'Listen, I'm sorry but I'm having a motorised chair delivered tomorrow, so I don't need you to come any more.'

Reg says nothing, unsure how to respond.

'Reg?'

'I'm here... That's good then. You didn't say you'd ordered one.'

Darren puts his hand over the receiver and swears. 'You know what I'm like these days; busy, busy. Sorry I just forgot.'

'All right, lad. Maybe we could have a coffee though; for old time's sake.'

'Let's do that. Thanks for everything, old man. You've been a real life saver.' Darren hesitates, hating himself for lying about the chair, then disconnects. He sits motionless; feels a sadness that surprises him. But it passes and he wakes up his laptop to see if Tanya is about.

Two days later Darren's laptop crashes. He stares disbelieving at the black screen, at its refusal to start. He presses the space bar, the power switch, the escape button, all of them faster and harder. He shouts obscenities at it, throws the manual across the room. Still the screen remains unblinking.

Darren rings his IT expert. 'When can you come and fix it? It's my life!'

'Things are a bit backed up at the moment, Darren. I'll get to you as soon as I can, I promise.'

'Please. I'm on benefits. I really can't afford to buy a replacement.'

He puts down his phone and chews at a broken fingernail, not knowing what else to do. The flat is silent. There is no sound from the road outside. Not even the hoped for sight of Mrs Patel. There's no one. Darren dials his old mate Gareth. A voice tells him the number is unobtainable. His throat is dry, his hands tremble. He wheels himself slowly over to the window and looks out. Hours pass. People hurry by, huddled in coats, looking forward to the warmth of family life. Not one glances his way.

In the coffee shop on the High Street, the girl stands at the window and scans the faces of those going past, her expression lifeless.

Winter Solstice
Carole Lynch

There it will be, that moment;

the turning point

when there is only the long dark night ahead

and all light is extinguished.

That astronomical phenomenon, the axial tilt of your earth

will spin you away into another orbit altogether,

lost even to yourself.

It is certain to be a Blue Christmas

while I await the rebirth of the sun gods, alone.

Driven

John O'Connor

I'm not sure if that's when I had the idea; in fact I'm certain that it wasn't then, not right away in any case. But that was when it started.

The road that passes the hospital is quite wide, tree lined and pleasant. The houses look like the kind of places where well-to-do families once lived, but which are now what are known to the authorities as HIMOs - Houses In Multiple Occupation - bedsits to you and me. Of course not all of them are like this. One or two remain as individual homes, or as single flats. These are the well-kept ones, generally. As I drove past that morning it was these thoughts which occupied my mind, not the parked cars or the pedestrian crossing, nor the 'Slow - School' sign, and certainly not the speed limit of 30 miles per hour. So when the interactive sign flashed on I was a little taken aback. I'd not noticed it before, on its slender grey pole, half hidden by the swaying branches of a magnificent Plane tree. But there it was, shouting its order at me like a furious, red-faced school master. 'Slow down! 30 mph!' I confess it made me smile. You see mine was the only car moving on the street, so it couldn't have meant anyone else. It had to be me that it was so angry at, me who had incurred its wrath, me who it had spotted and chosen to admonish. And in that moment I realised that, unless something extraordinary happened, this would probably be the only time that anything - or anyone - paid me the slightest bit of attention that day.

I made a point of always using that route to the library after that, swooshing past the gates of the Lady Bowering Preparatory School, seeing all the 'yummy mummies' in their 4 x 4s, imagining the tutting and pinched lips which accompanied their disapproving stares as I activated the grumpy sign, as I called it, by doing precisely thirty-five miles per hour past its glare. Of course it was only a matter of time before this little game lost its appeal. Like, I imagined, a drug addict who starts out just trying a few puffs on a joint but then becomes accustomed to the buzz and needs something stronger, I felt the urge to increase the adrenaline rush that breaking the law had given me. I would have to do something fairly radical, right? I decided to take a different route one morning, slightly longer it was true, but one which took me out onto the dual carriageway which skirted the town centre and provided an effective by-pass for anyone with somewhere else to be. This stretch of road was subject to a 50 mph limit. There were no cameras, no interactive signs, no automated methods of controlling the speed of traffic whatsoever. No, on this road, if you were going to break the law you would only be noticed if there was a good old fashioned Bobby in a Panda car patrolling along its length. And it didn't take me very long to find him.

It was a Friday, I remember that. Brian, my husband, always went out on Friday evenings after work. That meant that he would be home late and he would be drunk, not roaring mind, but drunk enough to be angry and sulky if I mentioned Katie. If I stayed quiet though, then he would just raid the fridge, sit on the sofa in front of the television and fall asleep, often without us having exchanged a word. And in the morning

I would be up and out of the door before he came to, so that I wouldn't have to face him and deal with any complaints about the state of the house, my lack of a job, the way I looked, or anything else. I usually went to the library to work on my book, or to the park, just to sit and watch people. And so it went on, week in and week out, month after month, just as it had done since Katie died. I had become anonymous; just another grieving mother. Oh I could have started a campaign - that's what people in my situation do isn't it? Campaign, call for change, raise money. But I wasn't interested in all that. Besides, who really cared? No, there had to be a better way.

When it finally happened the policeman couldn't have been more charming.

'Good morning madam, any particular reason for the excessive speed?'

'No officer,' I replied demurely. 'I'm sorry, I simply wasn't paying attention. What is the speed limit on here, only it is a dual carriageway isn't it?'

He let me off with a friendly warning and I should have been grateful for that, but that's not at all what I was after. So the next time I was *much* ruder:

'Haven't you lot got anything better to do? You should be out catching rapists and murderers' - all that sort of stuff poured out of my mouth. I ended up with a hefty fine and three points on my licence. This was more like it.

The 'big one', as I called it, happened on a wet Friday morning when everyone else had slowed down because there was a horse or something loose on the carriageway. I drove straight at the car in front of me, only swerving at the last moment and hitting it, and another car, in the process. One was driven by a young girl who reminded me a little of our Katie, except that she started blubbering and carrying on about how cross her dad was going to be, something Katie would never have done. The other car was driven by a flash bugger in a BMW, who immediately got on his mobile 'phone and started demanding that the police attend and breathalyse everyone involved. They did attend, I was breathalysed and I did fail. Polishing off a couple of whiskys that morning for breakfast had ensured that I'd be over the limit.

The police station was warmer and brighter than I remembered it, and the staff there were positively lovely - maybe something to do with my age and the fact that I showed such a high level of remorse. I was charged of course, I went to Court and was banned from driving for twelve months. I learnt very little that time. Also Brian hardly noticed. He carried on as if nothing had happened mainly because for him, I suppose, nothing had. That's his way you see, just to carry on, pretend it never happened, shut it out. For me, travelling by bus everywhere at least meant that someone had to acknowledge my existence, even if it was only the driver saying 'thanks love' when I paid my fare, and of course sitting in a library writing is a certain way of being left undisturbed. Undisturbed and ignored.

It was during one of these sessions that I first noticed him. Scruffy, like a lost dog, his long, straggly hair and scuffed leather jacket made most people give him a wide berth. The lady at the desk handed him a card and pointed him in the direction of the bank of free computers along the far wall. He perched himself on a stool and began tapping away at the keyboard. When he left, half an hour later, so did I. I followed him through the town and into several large stores. He didn't notice me at all - why would he? Eventually he went into the park and met up with a group of other young men, all standing or laying around on benches, some swigging from bottles and cans or smoking heaven knows what. I walked up to them and told them that they were disgusting, that they made the place look untidy, that they should get jobs. One of them, slightly drunk, swung his can at me and shouted some expletives in my face.

Then the one in the leather jacket who I'd followed grabbed his arm and told him to stop. He turned to me and said, 'Eff off love, for your own good.'

I got a good look at him then, before walking back towards the entrance and out of the park.

My next stop was Boots. I knew they had store detectives there and sure enough I spotted the plain-looking lady with the outsize handbag, browsing aimlessly amongst the aisles. I shoved a couple of bottles of some fancy hair stuff into my own bag and made straight for the exit.

At first I didn't think she'd seen it, but as I stepped outside I felt a hand on my shoulder. 'Excuse me, I have reason to believe that you have something you haven't paid for.'

In the office my insistence on not being searched unless and until, as I put it bluntly, a *real* police officer was present, ensured they wouldn't just warn me, ban me and throw me out. And so I was soon back at the police station, dealt with this time by a surly female detective, and it was here that, by listening carefully, I picked up more snippets, more names. I was cautioned, and then let go.

Two days later I saw him at the library again. He had smartened himself up a little but it was him.

I approached and whispered, 'I know what you do.'

He looked angrily at me, but neither of us could raise our voices because of where we were.

'Look love,' he hissed, 'I don't know who you are or what you want but leave me alone, right.'

His breath stank, making me recoil. I followed him outside where he spun around and swore at me again.

'I saw you shoplifting - in Marks,' I said.

He glared at me, but there was a hint of fear in his face too. I liked that. It made me feel better; stronger.

'You're a shoplifter, and a drug dealer too, I'll bet.'

'You the Old Bill?' He looked more worried now.

'Yes', I said.

He looked around, then laughed.

'Fuck off love, you ain't the Old Bill.'

'Ok, I'm not,' I told him, 'but I could go to them, with what I know about you. I've been following you for weeks. I know everything you do, every scheme you're mixed up in.'

He started to walk off.

'I can help you,' I shouted. The loudness of my voice brought him back.

He stood close. 'I don't need your help. I don't need no one, right.'

'I need some... some gear.' I said.

'You what?' He looked incredulous.

'Gear,' I said, 'drugs, you know.'

'Are you for real?' Then he laughed.

'I've got money, look.' I opened my purse and showed him the cash I'd drawn out of the bank that morning.

'There's £200 there,' I said. 'What will that get me?'

He shuffled his feet, looking around him, then said, 'Follow me,' oblivious to the irony.

He took me to a car park underneath Lidl's, making phone calls all the time as we walked, and it was during one of them that I heard the name that I'd wanted to hear. Jess. The little bitch who'd given the pills to our - to my - Katie, the ones that had killed her on that warm, beautiful summer evening last August, when everything had seemed perfect, and she had been so happy, so full of life and promise. She probably thought she'd got away with it. The police had given up on their investigation, citing a lack of evidence. But, I knew. I'd found out. And it didn't take me long to meet her after that. Nor did it take me long to finish her life, just as she'd finished Katie's and, by doing so, finished ours too. Now suddenly, it seemed, everybody took notice of me.

Yorkshire Bear

Frederic Stansfield

The old train rattled into Grizzlewick Station. We got up from the dusty bus seats. Dad lugged our cases to the diesel unit's doorway and handed them down the steps. Mummy placed the luggage on the low station platform. She got me and my sister Kate to stand next to the cases. When we had got everything out of the train, Dad climbed down to join us.

'We're here at last,' he said.

The train belched a cloud of diesel fumes from the pipe between its two carriages. It growled its way towards the tunnel that led across towards Manchester. We were left alone in the dark grey dusk.

'Come on, Darren, pick up your bag,' Dad said. It was a little case in the shape of a pink elephant. I had been given it specially for this journey.

We followed Dad down a steep street to a bridge over the canal. There was an inn where day- trippers could watch barges going through the lock on a summer day.

'Can I have a room looking over the canal?' I asked.

'Maybe some other time.' Dad replied. 'We're staying in the village.'

Dad led us along a couple more streets of small houses. There was a pub next door to a derelict factory. Most of the windows in the mill were broken; but the pub, with its soot stained bricks, was still open.

We went inside. Dad rang a bell on the counter. After a minute or two a sharp-faced lady appeared behind the empty bar.

'We're the Smiths. We've booked to stay two nights,' Dad said.

'Hello.' The sharp-faced landlady ruffled my hair. I scowled. Then she went to pick up my little sister. Mummy got there first.

'Kate's shy,' she said.

The landlady led us to a first floor room which could sleep all four of us. It had an old red carpet with threadbare patches. Its stains smelt of stale beer. An old washstand stood in one corner.

'The toilet is upstairs,' the landlady said. 'Come downstairs when you have freshened up.'

The meal was at a table in the corner of the bar. I ate enough of the minced beef and potatoes to make my parents happy. Then I was ready to sleep after the long journey.

It wasn't any better in the morning.

'Eat up your porridge. It's good for you.' The landlady said.

I had never eaten porridge made with just water and salt. It looked thin and runny. I didn't fancy it. I pushed the bowl away. 'Shan't.'

'Please bring Darren a glass of orange squash. He doesn't drink tea.' Mummy said.

'It'll be extra,' the landlady said.

'That's all right.'

After breakfast Mummy got me and Kate ready. She brushed my hair, made me do up my shoelaces and put on my coat. Then we all set off for the nursing home.

'We mustn't be late. Great-Granny will be expecting us,' Dad said.

We walked up the hill until we reached the Manchester Road. It let the cars and lorries avoid the centre of the village. On the other side of the road a dozen boys were kicking a football around a small playing field.

'Can I play?' I asked Dad.

'No, we've got to get to the nursing home.'

'Please,' I insisted.

'We haven't time.' Dad took me firmly by the hand as we set off along the footpath beside the Manchester Road. A stream of traffic swished past us.

Grizzlewick was too poor to have large detached houses that could be converted into homes for the elderly. We had to walk for a mile until we reached a large new building. A footpath led up a steep bank to the entrance of the nursing home.

Mummy made herself known at the reception desk.

'Mrs Oldthwaite is looking forward to seeing you. She gets so few visitors,' the nurse said.

'It's not so easy now that my mother has passed away,' Mummy said. 'Her daughter shared her house here in Grizzlewick; but we live in Margate. I can't get away during term time.'

The nurse led us down a long corridor. A cleaner was mopping the floor. It smelt of polish.

We were ushered into a room at the far end of the building. The door had been left open but the room still gave off a stuffy odour.

'Look who's here to see you, Mrs Oldthwaite,' the nurse said cheerily.

Great-Granny was slumped in an armchair. The television was on but she wasn't looking at it.

'You're here at last. Couldn't you have come earlier?' Great-Granny glared at Mummy.

'We came as soon as we could.' Mummy said. She leaned over to give Great-Granny a kiss.

'Look who's here. Darren,' Mummy said.

'Give me a kiss,' Great-Granny demanded.

'Go on, Darren,' Mummy said, nudging me forward.

I gave Great-Granny a peck on the cheek. It was stubbly, with white whiskers.

'You've grown,' Great-Granny said.

I had only met my Great-Granny once, three years before. She had been in her own home then, in one of the terraced houses. She had already started to forget things.

Mummy turned to my sister. 'This is Kate', she said.

Great-Granny looked blank, but she gave Kate a hug. Kate cried, so Mummy took her back and wiped her face.

'Who's the man?' Great-Granny exclaimed.

'Peter,' Mummy said. Dad leant over to give Great-Granny a kiss. Great-Granny didn't like it. To her, Dad was a stranger.

Mummy tried to make conversation; but it was hard.

'When's Dot coming?' Great-Granny asked.

'She's not. Dot got cancer.' Mummy blew her nose to stop her tears. Then she folded up a cardigan and put it on Great-Granny's lap. But there wasn't really much to say or do.

'We must be going now,' Mummy said after a few minutes.

'Come back tomorrow,' Great-Granny ordered. 'And tell Dot to come too.'

'Bye for now.' Mummy gave her grandmother a farewell kiss, wiping away another tear.

When we got back to the village, there were still half a dozen boys on the playing field. They were all wearing red football shirts. Some were Manchester United: Ferdinand, Giggs and Rooney. The others were Liverpool: Gerrard, Carragher and Torres.

'Can I join in?' I asked.

'Sure.'

But the mood changed when I took off my anorak. I was wearing a sweatshirt with the name of Frank Lampard, my hero at Chelsea.

'You're not from these parts.'

'No. I'm from Kent. We're visiting my gran.'

I tried playing first for the Man U lads and then the Liverpool ones. But it didn't matter. I got barged over either by the lad in the Gerrard shirt or by the boy in the Ferdinand one.

Kate saved the day. 'I want to go back,' she said.

'Southerner!' the other lads spat after me as I left. I was glad to get away. Anyway, Chelsea beats United and the Scousers these days.

There was a café in the village. My parents asked for tea, which was brought in two white cups. Kate and I had glasses of orange squash.

'You did your best,' Dad said to Mummy. 'You couldn't have done any more.'

'You did very well too, Darren,' Mummy added. 'Great-Granny remembered you.'

Opposite the Co-op in the main street there was a toy shop next to a ladies' hairdresser.

You've been so good, we can go inside,' Dad said.

The shop was really the front room of one of the terraced houses. A middle-aged lady sat at a desk near the entrance.

'Have a look round,' she said.

Most of the toys seemed to be for girls. There were dolls and boards on which you could put together jewellery. Instead of toy soldiers, guns and aeroplanes there were little ballerinas, fairies and dragons. I was disappointed. But then I saw a teddy bear at the back of the shop, it was dressed in an Edwardian sailor suit.

'Can I have the teddy bear?' I asked Dad.

'Here you are. The shopkeeper wrapped him up and handed him over. 'And he has a friend.' She wrapped up another bear, wearing a billowy blue polka dot dress, for Kate.

'They go together. It would break their hearts to separate them,' she said.

Dad hardly had time to pay for the bears before I ran out of the shop, full of glee. Kate tried to follow me, but she couldn't run as fast. Mum had to hold me back until my sister could catch up.

We returned to our room so that Kate and I could change into our trainers.

'She'll keep warm until this evening,' Kate said, putting her bear on her bed.

'I'm keeping my Captain Bear with me,' I said.

'We'll go to the top of the hill,' Dad said. He led the way across the footbridge at the station and up a sheep track that started behind a farm on the other die of the station. Grizzlewick was already six hundred feet up, so it took us less than an hour's walk until the moor flattened out and we reached a Survey Point. Dad stood me on top of the concrete pillar. I could see across to Lancashire.

'Look, Captain Bear!' I exclaimed, holding up my teddy. 'The Irish Sea's over there. We'll find you a battleship to sail.'

It started to rain.

'We must get down to the village before it gets worse,' Dad said. But we had left it too late. Within a few minutes it was pelting down and the temperature had dropped. I began to feel cold. It was not until we got as far as the farm that I noticed.

'Where's Captain Bear?' I screamed. 'We must go back and find him.'

'It's far too wet, Darren.' Dad said. 'You'll catch a cold.' He grasped my hand to ensure I didn't try to find my toy.

I howled all the way back to the inn, and I wasn't any better over supper.

'We can share my bear.' Kate said.

'No. She's your bear.' Dad said to Kate. 'And we can't go back to the toyshop, Darren. The lady expected you to look after Captain Bear. But I'll buy you another toy back in Kent.'

No bear in Margate could be a patch on Captain Bear. I wept myself to sleep but woke up during the night

'Where's my bear?' I cried out.

In the morning, the weather had cleared up.

'You go and see Great-Granny again.' Dad said. 'I'll go for another walk with the children.'

Dad took us on the same path across the footbridge and up the track beyond the farmhouse. I kept trying to look either side of the track just in case my bear was there. I even looked in a ditch, filling my trainer full of squelchy water.

'I want my Captain Bear,' I sobbed. 'Find my bear.'

It wasn't until we got near the Survey Point that everything changed. Somebody had propped the bear up against the concrete pillar. His sailor suit was torn and muddy; but it was definitely my Captain Bear. I ran the last hundred yards flat out and snatched him up.

'You've come back!' I cried out with joy. 'I'll never let you go again.'

I hugged Captain Bear close to my chest all the way back to the village.

That was five years ago. I've never been to Yorkshire since then. Four months after our trip, Kate and I stayed for a couple of days with Aunty Becky whilst my parents drove up to Grizzlewick. Mummy looked very sad. Since then we have always gone abroad for holidays, or to my Dad's parents' in Dorset.

Mummy washed my teddy bear. She also sewed up the tear in his sailor suit, so he is nearly as good as new. Captain Bear will remind me of Grizzlewick for the rest of my life.

Numbers

Emma Collins

Two dogs are buried in the back garden of this house and also one tortoise and one bird. The bird had been found by me with a bloody injury and died despite my then seven-year old's expertise in 'nursing'. A funeral had duly been held, where I had said some words.

What are other numbers are there then in this house to represent my life and my time of living in it?

One marriage, two births, one death. Forty-two years this house had been owned by us. Three days on the market. Sold. Five hundred and twelve thousand in pounds.

Fifteen minutes now until the new occupants arrive and I, the very old occupant, leave.

Four. The amount of nursing homes my daughter has viewed before finding the 'perfect' one.

Twelve. The amount of weeks it took to her to convince me that this place was too much for me now.

One. Step I take off the little stool. Three breaths I take before the numbers end.

The Door

Emma Collins

She wears her hair in the same way she did fifteen years ago, that much hasn't changed. It's lighter than before but Ed has the feeling she's done that to cover the grey that has surely started to creep in. Her eyes look smaller, her lips thinner. As Ed stands with his hand on the pub door, ready to go in, he hesitates. How much of the girl he once knew is in the woman before him?

Did she still take bubble baths late at night with a glass of wine in hand? Did she still argue her points passionately with such utter conviction? Did she still listen so intently that you could believe you were the only other person in the world?

He catches sight of himself in the pub window. The beginning of a paunch, thinning hair, thick eyebrows burrowed in thought. He checks his watch; Shelley would be halfway through the torturous routine of bath and bed, secure in the knowledge that he was out with clients finalising a deal. He'd set the story up last week as his heart raced half thrilled, half disgusted.

A step further will take him over a threshold not yet crossed. The woman looks up from the table and sees him. She smiles shyly at him and he feels the years slip away. He sucks in his stomach, pulls back his shoulders and opens the door.

Vigil

Emma Collins

Hilda hasn't been home for a week. Now, each night when the dark has come, I hear a key in the door and a voice calling my name gently. I ignore the voice and only venture down when it has gone.

I ravage the food that has been left then go back to the bedroom window, looking out of the side of the nets to continue my vigil.

The one she calls Helen returns night after night, stopping only to call my name. Her voice has become a plea but still I refuse to leave my post.

She misses an evening and my stomach is growling when I hear the key in the lock. I come to her this time; I can't help but feel something has changed. Helen's face is red and her eyes are puffy.

'She gone puss, she's gone. Mum has gone.' She scoops me up and head buried in my fur, she weeps.

Drunken Lost Night Out

Joe McMullen

After a wild lost night out I opened my eyes to find a scarily ugly woman lying beside me. It was then I realised I had arrived home safely. Another night to remember or forget depends on the state of your head I suppose. But who was the woman laying in bed next to me? She wasn't number six Stella my regular at Bad Billy's Bar was number six. I gently prodded the dozing young woman and asked rather foolishly 'Are you number six?' She opened bloodshot eyes smiled and went back to dozing. At least she's not anaemic I thought as I dragged myself out of bed. But where is Stella not like her to miss the chance of an early breakfast and perhaps something small.

I could hear my manservant James banging around in the kitchen he always did that when he knew I had a woman with me. He would have to clean up after her. He knew she would be another manner less hooker who would leave pillows and bed sheets smelling, spend hours in the shower probably the first shower she'd ever had. He hated having to clean up after them. It is demeaning for an African male servant to clean up after women. Washing ladies' underwear and cleaning toilets are not chores any male servant will undertake.

There was another reason James did not want anybody else to get any perks from me, he was my manservant and as such assumed he had first call on anything I was giving away including money. Such is the culture among African servants.

After a shower I felt better but still not one hundred percent. Next, a long swig from a bottle of cold orange juice kept in the fridge for such an occasion. James watched me in his usual pretend manner of subservience as I opened the fridge door and took out the bottle. I lifted the bottle to check its contents and immediately noted the level amount in the bottle was above a mark I had scratched on the bottle the previous evening. I looked around to ask James how is it possible for the level to be above the mark? No point arguing the orange juice question with James he would admit nothing and remain head bowed hands together while the breakfast toast burned.

Realising he had been rumbled, James scarpered into the bedroom to chase the woman out of bed and out of the house. He shouted at the woman. 'WeWe kwenda haraka.' He then proceeded to make as much noise as possible, opening the windows and spraying every corner of the room as well as the bed, in an effort to encourage her to get a move on.

I could hear the swish-swish of Anthony's 'slasher' and his conversation with ladies on their way to market. I stepped outside. On sensing my presence Anthony stopped talking turned and faced me. 'Jambo sanaa Mzee,' then bent to the task of cutting the grass. He would carry on like that until I left for work then spend the rest of the day gossiping with James about my exploits of the previous evening.

Where was my car? I checked the side and front of the house watched by Anthony. No car.

I hurried back into the house. 'James, have you seen my car or do you know where it is?' 'No sir,' as he pointed out that my breakfast was on the table. Silly question, even if he knew he wouldn't tell me, although I was sure full details of my evening escapade would have been passed on to both James and Anthony by the night watchman.

The young lady appeared from the bedroom and waited for her money. What for? I thought to ask her what we did all night. I gave her the equivalent of twenty British Pounds in Kenya Shillings and she left with unkind comments from James and Anthony ringing in her ears.

A neighbour dropped me off at Bad Billy's Bar. I needed to find Stella. John Karatunga was already at work behind the bar and smiled as I walked in; a knowing smile. He offered me a beer on the house. I declined. I explained to him that I had come to see if Stella was okay and find out where my car was. Apparently it was about three am when we left the bar and I was in a poor state. Derek, along with three accompanying females, had finally got me into Derek's car and rummaged in my pockets for my car keys. I remained with the girls while Derek moved my car to the rear of the bar. John Karatunga explained to me that Stella had left and returned to her home village and she had left a note for me with Derek.

He further assured me the replacement girl Muna, the new number six, was every bit as beautiful as Stella and was looking forward to meeting me as soon as possible.

I never saw or heard from the young lady I found in my bed that morning; just another near miss.

The Gift of the Gab
Michael Burney-Cumming

Terry Sheldon puts down the phone and stares at the frosted glass in the office door 'Samson's International Removers'. What a joke. They hardly leave Kent these days let alone the country. With housing market as it is, going anywhere is a bonus. The phone call from Thelma has done little to cheer him up. She has been doing the books for years and now it is all bad news. He sits and thinks about the scheme they have cooked up. It isn't much but it is better than nothing.

'A word in your shell-like.'

Dave looks up from page three of The Sun. 'What?'

'I want a word,' says Terry.

'When?'

'Now.'

Frowning, Dave picks up his mug of tea and ambles past the shabby partition into Terry's office. 'What's this all about then?'

'Christmas, we need to talk about Christmas.'

'What about Christmas?'

'That's why we a need a meeting; it's delicate.'

'When?'

'When what?'

'When do you want the meeting?'

Idly, Terry flips back and forth through the blank pages of the big leather diary. His finger hovers over a blank space in an otherwise blank page. 'Here we go, Friday 26th November, four o'clock.'

'What's this all about? It sounds like bad news to me.'

'No, it's an opportunity,' says Terry. 'I got that from a bloke at Rotary. No such thing as a problem he said, only opportunities. We'll talk about it when we meet.'

Two weeks later, Dave strolls into Terry's office. Terry looks up and cocks his head to one side enquiringly.

'The meeting, you remember. About Christmas?'

'Oh yes, come in, shut the door. Right, I'm not going to beat about the bush. Too many people waste their lives talking about nothing, but not me. I like to come straight to the point. Mrs Sheldon has been nagging me for months to take her abroad to Bolivia so she can live in style. So I have decided. I'm going to retire at Christmas.

'I know, I know, I am only sixty–two at the end of the month, but I've got a little nest egg, policies maturing, and the like. I'm getting to old for this lark. Anyway, I've decide to sell you the business at Christmas for five hundred pounds. How long have you worked here? Thirteen years isn't it? You're the one with the ideas, like the Christmas tree deliveries and I reckon you'll make a go of it. There's no hurry, I don't need an answer now. Think about it over the weekend and let me know Monday. If you're not interested, then I'll offer it to Big Arthur.'

Terry watches Dave gather his things and disappear out the door then he picks up the phone and calls Thelma.

'How did it go then?' she says. 'Did he buy it?'

'I think so, we'll know Monday.'

Thelma senses that Terry is not a happy bunny. She knows Terry feels bad about what they are doing but there is too much at stake for him to bottle out now. The business is a basket case. It can't even cover the overheads or the debts on the new vans. What a mess - and buying the vans seemed such a good move at the time.

'Good, the Enterprise Loan from the Government came in today, so we can add that to the pot,' says Thelma. 'You all right, then?'

'Yeah, I suppose so. If it's Dave or me then it sure as hell is not going to be me. Yeah, I am all right. I will be even better when you've transferred the funds and we're on that plane.' Terry puts down the phone and reaches for the mug of cold coffee on the desk.

Di watches as Dave carefully puts down the mug of tea and starts to smother the fish fingers and chips with ketchup.

'So, what does your Dad say about it?' she asks.

'He says go for it, but I don't know. Terry is up to something. The business is going down the pan. Terry just sits in his office all day making phone calls to his mates at Rotary. When I suggest we try something different he just rubbishes my ideas.'

'Have we got the money?' says Di.

'Yeah, in the car fund we have.'

'Well, you would be your own boss and the lease has still got twenty years to run.'

'Yeah, but why only a monkey?' says Dave. 'He could sell it for a lot more than that.'

'But it would take him ages and a lot of hassle. You are always saying he hates hassle,' says Di. 'Look, why not take a punt for once? You have done the same job since you left school. We have lived in this place, four doors from your mum's, since we got married. I know its old but the car will last us another few years. It might be fun. You know, being the boss's wife.'

It's January the first and when Dave arrives at the office he stops and takes a deep breath, savouring the heady mixture of bleach, furniture polish and cheap paint. He and Di have slaved all over the holiday to clean the place up. He puts the kettle on and takes the tea back to Terry's office. No, no *my* office, still can't get that right, he thinks. He pulls the young executive brief case, that Di has given him for Christmas, across the desk and opens it. Taking the list out he looks at the first item, finding a new accountant. How do you do that? Leaning back, he looks around. It all seems so empty, now that Terry has gone.

Out

Jo Gamgee

Once upon a time there was a kitten called...But no, his name is not important. This is his story.

I arrived in cupped hands. As I searched for the comfort of fur and the smell of home they were discussing what to call me. Their words went around in a loop: Topcat, Pusscat, Pussin, Pushkin, Poshcat, Pippin. None of this concerned me. I hid under the bed, behind the curtain and in the washing basket but could not settle. I slept on any cushion, pillow, pile of ironing, or bed not chosen for me. I also looked out of the window.

At last I was let out. It was not long before I was in neighbouring gardens, over fences and climbing high up into a tree. A cat must spread its wings. At dawn and at dusk I liked to lie on a comfortable branch, feel gentle breezes ruffle my fur and sniff the sweet air. I stayed in my leafy green hideaway to listen to the songs of the birds by day and watch the moon and stars move across the sky by night. This world was to be my home and the creatures of the woods and fields my companions.

It's fair enough for a family to go away once in a while and if there had be to someone *in loco parentis*, the neighbour from number 9 was the obvious choice, because she was always at home. Miss Craze, a retired teacher, was keen to take responsibility for me, as she rather worryingly put it. When the family got into the car, the mother said, 'He likes to stay out at night.'

'He's a wanderer,' said the boy.

'He often goes missing,' added the girl, rather sadly.

'He's a cat,' laughed the father.

Oh, dear, thought Miss Craze, smiling a worried smile. 'Have a lovely time,' she said aloud, waving as the car drove off.

Things began amicably enough. I took a nap under my favourite bush in her garden on the first afternoon and did not protest when I was picked up, carried indoors at six o'clock and locked in for the night. After all, there had to be give and take on both sides. But as soon as Miss Craze opened up bright and early at 5.30 the next morning, I was out over the garden fence exploring, happily occupied stalking in the long grass, until I returned around four o'clock for my nap under the bush. I kept half an eye open to avoid another night locked in. To me a house is not a home. It is a refuge in times of storm and stress, where I can top up with fast food and sleep without keeping one eye open.

Off I went, through hedgerows and over ditches, rejoicing as my territory expanded. I expected Miss Craze to have a good grasp of this as I had spotted her reading T S Eliot only a few days before, in preparation for her responsibilities. Try to see it from my point of view. The ginger tom, who is no match for me in looks or physique, is nevertheless a rival and I have to be physically present night and day in case a female strolls across my path. A young cat needs to be out there. What a wonderful welcome I got from the neighbours when I walked back in to the garden three days and three nights later. They were all outside enjoying the sunshine, discussing my whereabouts. It's nice to be missed. 'Pippin's here! There's Pip! Where have you been, Poppet? Who's a naughty Pusskin? Good boy, Pushkin. What have you been up to, Pussin? Did you miss us, Puss?' Did I what? Perhaps I looked a little different. I was elated. And I am not all bad. I did catch a mouse and leave it on Miss Craze's doorstep as a surprise.

Fourteen hours later I awoke feeling marvellous; all set to resume my adventures. If only. Miss Craze was out of sorts. Why did she keep repeating herself? 'You're staying in today. It's for your own good. Better safe than sorry,' and so on. I blame her misspent years training dogs, who may well go 'into bed' if told to do so *ad nauseam*. Let them. Plead, scold, do whatever you like, all is futile. Miss Craze, it seems, is slow to learn.

As some sort of peace offering I was invited to her house in the afternoons to watch tennis. You see my problem. 'What larks, Pip, old chap, what larks.' Where does she get this stuff from? There was only one way to play this. My way.

Miss Craze claims to find tennis engrossing, but sometimes dozes off, because of the repetitive nature of the game. Choosing my moment, I went to check upstairs. The bathroom window was open and I was able to spring onto the porch roof in a trice. It was the noise of shampoo bottles crashing to the floor that sent her rushing upstairs, then downstairs, then out of the front door to see me descending backwards down the wooden trellis. She was surprised, 'Well, I never,' but not impressed, 'You little rascal.' I am not little.

It was a black day indeed, when I was tied to the garden tap with a collar and lead, while she watered the garden. I felt the call of the wild. One deft pull and I had released the collar and was rolling on the grass. Her jaw and the hose dropped, as she made a dash in my direction. 'You little monkey!' Little, again. From my vantage point on the top of the fence she looked sheepish and drenched.

Towards the end of the week things became easier. Miss Craze was learning to shrug her shoulders. All I had to do was bide my time. My goodness, can that woman talk on the telephone? Mostly about what larks we had. I slunk silently upstairs. Just as I hoped, her bedroom door opened to my touch. In seconds I was out of the open window, making the long descent to mingle with the creatures of the night.

Miss Craze was ticking off the days on the calendar. Three days and nights absent without leave and three escapes had left us both tired. I decided we needed a rest. After all, I didn't want to wipe the floor with her. There was still fun to be had indoors chasing the mouse on her desk. No doubt tales will be told about how catlike I was to stay out for days on end, returning home looking like something the dog brought in. Little do they know. Those three days and nights down in the town with Katya, the Cathedral cat, were three of the best days of my life. But that is another story.

About the Authors

Michael Burney-Cumming took up creative writing in the autumn of 2011 after attending an U3A taster session. He has since attended several creative writing workshops and adult education classes. He now writes poetry, plays, and short stories. He continues to work at broadening his understanding of the creative writing process and building his skills.

Brought up in care, **Caroline Cannons** graduated from Sheffield University in 1979 and worked in education for over thirty years. Her short stories for adults and children are published in numerous anthologies. A founder member of Canterbury Yarners, she promotes creative writing for all through public readings of her work.

Emma Collins is an avid reader and as a result of this passion for words began to write her own short stories from a young age. Her master plan is to give this all up when her blockbuster novel (as yet unwritten) is made into a blockbuster film.

Jo Gamgee's interests are music, languages, singing, reading, writing and walking. Her book *German for Musicians* (Faber) was written while teaching at the Royal Northern College of Music. Where would she be without books? Let's just say that the year in which all her books were in storage was a testing time. As a writer, Jo enjoys the sense of being alone and yet not alone. Readers know all about this.

Carol Hyde hails from Australia where she completed two degrees; the second in creative writing. She has had a number of feature articles published. Her stories in this anthology are the first of her fiction work to be published. Carol's aim is to entertain herself and others through short stories – oh, and world domination.

Carole Lynch published two text books, taught Psychology, and worked in the NHS before writing full time. Her short stories can be found in various publications and, as a founder member of the Canterbury Yarners, she regularly reads her work at literary festivals and other venues. She is currently preparing a short story collection.

Valerie Moffit grew up in Northumberland and still misses the hills and coastline of home. After a career in the civil service she is pleased to be jubilada and to have more time to spend learning Spanish, singing and writing stories. She is also researching the history of her Newcastle family.

John O'Connor lives in the heart of Kent with his wife, teenage daughter, four goldfish, three African land snails and a Border Collie called Whisper. The numbers for the smaller animals may vary from time to time; the others hopefully won't. A constant, nagging desire to write has led to an eclectic mix of short stories, half-finished books and many scraps of paper.

Frederic Stansfield moved to Ramsgate last year. Previously he lived in Canterbury. His most recent work was as a telephone operative in a call centre. He has also been a systems analyst and a university researcher. Frederic has previously published stories in Canterbury Yarns and poetry for SaveAs.